ZANY Can Do Anything

Nichole Hansen
Tevin Hansen

Handersen Publishing, LLC
Lincoln, Nebraska

Meet Zany

(pronounced z-ay-knee)

Zany is a unicorn with a unique point of view.
Each day is an adventure full of new things to
see, do, and try.

It's going to be a great day!

Zany knows that being prepared and picking out the perfect outfit are important parts of every experience.

✓ **Safari hat**
　　–to explore.

✓ **Star glasses**
　　–to see the sights.

✓ **Superhero cape**
　　–for saving the day.

✓ **Grass skirt**
　　–because it's awesome!

Now I am ready for anything!

Zany also has lists of things to do.

Some are silly.

- Dress up like a clown
- Learn to juggle
- Sing the ABCs backwards

Some are helpful.

- Clean my room
- Make lots of friends
- Learn to bake a carrot cake

Some are challenging.

- Beat Dad at Scrabble
- Win the big game
- Make a comic book

Some are even a little scary.

- Go mountain climbing
- Visit a haunted house
- try out for the school play

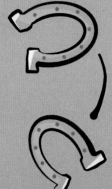

to do always:

- Dream Big
- Work Hard
- Be Yourself

#getzany

Like most unicorns, Zany loves sweets. But Zany also knows that the best way to start the day is with a breakfast full of fruits and veggies.

Blueberry muffins

Banana pudding

Apple pie

Zucchini bread

On the way to school, Zany likes to dream about things to learn and try.

Zany thinks about learning to dance.
There are so many different styles to try.

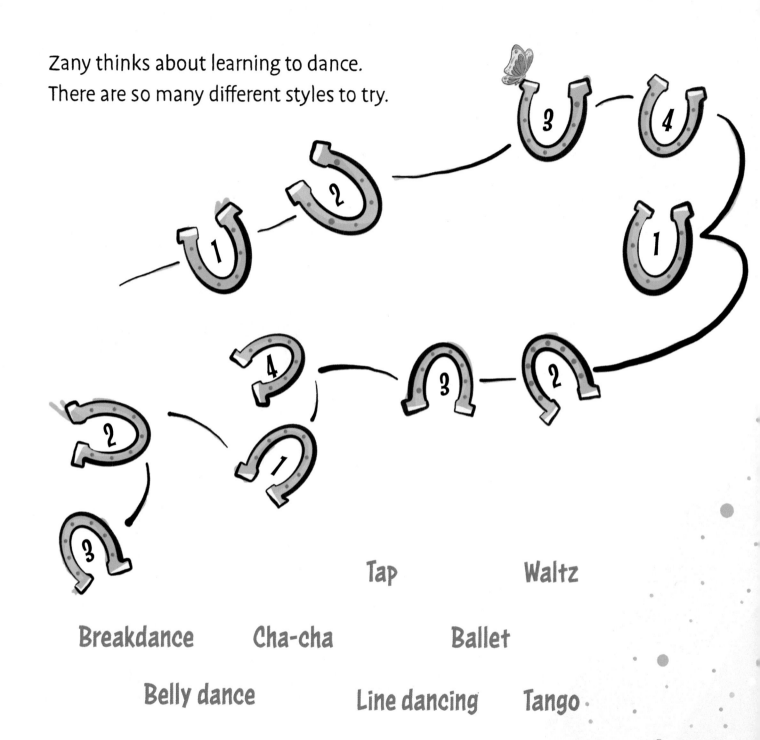

Tap

Waltz

Breakdance   Cha-cha   Ballet

Belly dance   Line dancing   Tango

I love to boogie.

And Disco

Then Zany dreams about playing every kind of music.

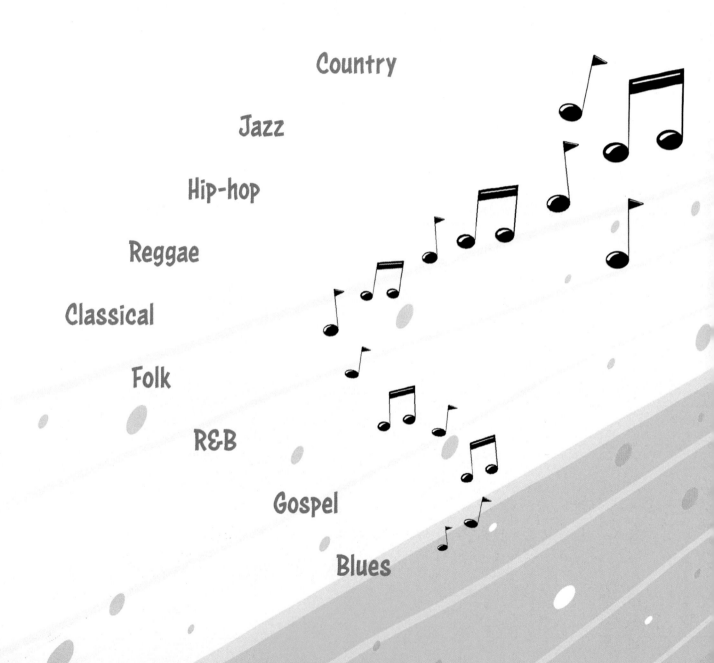

Country

Jazz

Hip-hop

Reggae

Classical

Folk

R&B

Gospel

Blues

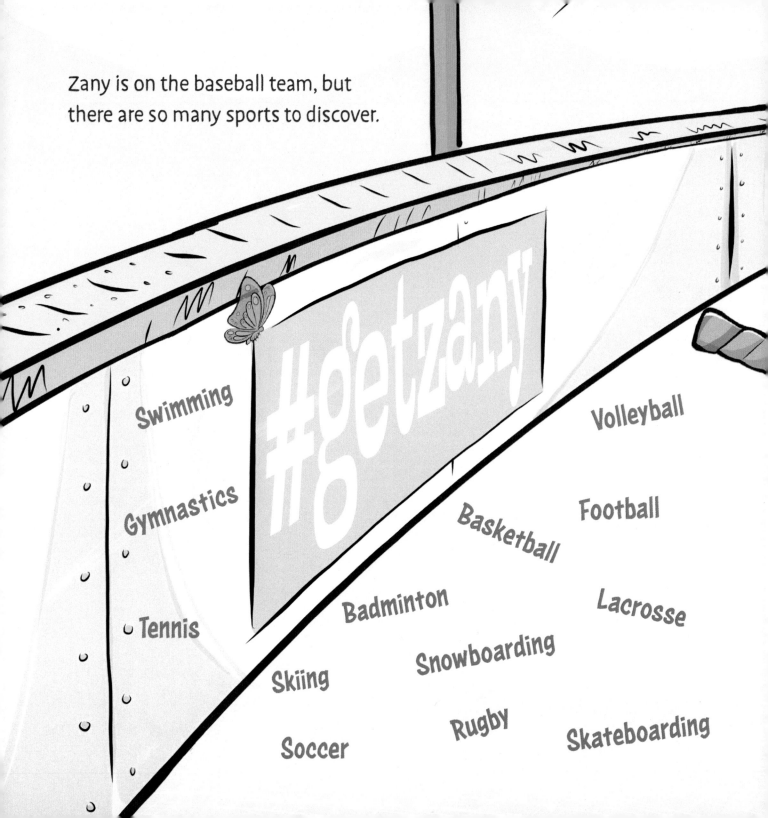

Zany is on the baseball team, but there are so many sports to discover.

When it comes to creating art, Zany loves experimenting with lots of supplies.

Every picture may not be perfect, but each one has its own unique style.

Just like Zany.

Glitter glue

Glitter paint

Glitter tape

Glitter paper

Glitter crayons

After school, Zany goes to the library. Because in books, you can learn about so many new things.

You start with picture books.

Then chapter books,

graphic novels,

and non-fiction.

If you have a library card, you can even take books home with you.

There is also a helpful librarian to assist you in finding...

just the right book.

there is so much to learn!

But no matter what Zany is wearing, or eating, or learning, or discovering...Zany always remembers three things.

1

Work Hard

New things aren't always easy.
They take hard work.

And it's okay to make mistakes,
as long as you do your best and
keep trying.

2

Be Yourself

There is only one you. Be a rockstar, try hockey, or make some art.

If you want to sing the ABCs backwards, then learn how!

JUST BE YOU!

3

Dream Big

The world is full of wonderful things to explore.

You can do anything.

Don't be afraid to

DREAM BIG.

But working hard and dreaming big can be tiring. That's why Zany also loves quiet time.

Dreaming about new things to try tomorrow.

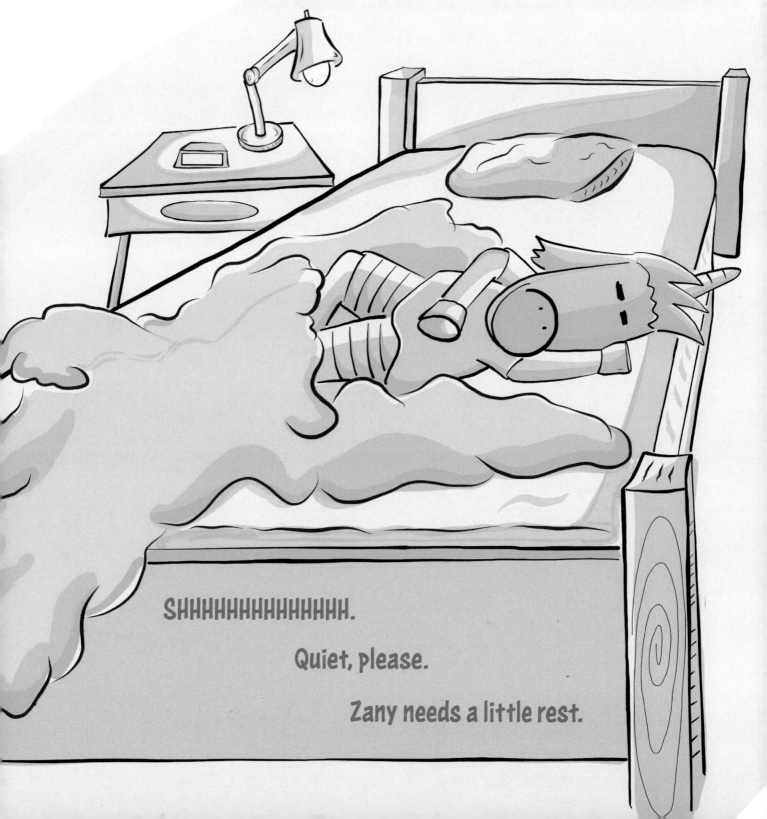

SHHHHHHHHHHHHHH.

Quiet, please.

Zany needs a little rest.

Nichole Hansen

Nichole Hansen lives in Nebraska with her husband and two children. She has been an avid reader since childhood, and still prefers books for young readers to any other out there, except maybe Jane Austen.

www.nicholehansen.com

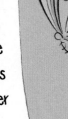

Tevin Hansen

tevin Hansen is an author and musician from Nebraska. He enjoys making music videos with his family. You can check them out on his Youtube channel or visit his website.

www.tevinhansen.com

For all the zany unicorns out there.

Handersen Publishing
Lincoln, Nebraska USA

Zany Can Do Anything

Text copyright © 2020 Nichole Hansen and Tevin Hansen

Illustrations copyright © 2020 Tevin Hansen

Cover copyright © 2020 Handersen Publishing, LLC

Library of Congress Cataloging-in-Publication Data

Names: Hansen, Nichole, 1982- author. | Hansen, Tevin, illustrator.

Title: Zany can do anything / Nichole Hansen, Tevin Hansen.

Description: Lincoln, Nebraska : Handersen Publishing, 2020. | Audience: Ages 0-7. | Audience: Grades K-1. | Summary: "Zany the unicorn knows that the best way to dream big is by being yourself and working hard"-- Provided by publisher.

Identifiers: LCCN 2019044939 (print) | LCCN 2019044940 (ebook) | ISBN 9781647039004 (paperback) | ISBN 9781647030001 (hardback) | ISBN 9781647030018 (Kindle edition)

Classification: LCC PZ7.1.H364325 Zan 2020 (print) | LCC PZ7.1.H364325 (ebook) | DDC [E]--dc23

LC record available at https://lccn.loc.gov/2019044939

LC ebook record available at https://lccn.loc.gov/2019044940

Publisher Website: www.handersenpublishing.com

Publisher Email: editors@handersenpublishing.com

Made in the USA
Middletown, DE
12 March 2022

62515664R00020